ARE YOU

A

DICKHEAD?

ARE YOU

A

DICKHEAD?

Fred Mogura

Simple Logic Publications

ARE YOU A DICKHEAD?

Disclaimer: This book has been created for the purpose of entertainment. The author and publisher make no representations or warranties of any kind with respect to this book or its contents. The author and publisher and any of its employees disclaim any and all liability for any damages arising out of or in connection with this book. This includes, but is not limited to, distress, offense or insult. Any use of this book or its content is at the reader's own risk.

ISBN 978-0-9872677-6-4 (Trade Paperback)

For more information, please contact the publisher at:
information@simplelogicpublications.com

Please note that we do not accept unsolicited manuscripts.

Illustrations under license from istockphoto.com

Printed in Australia • United States of America •
United Kingdom

Table of Contents

PART 2

GETTING AROUND...37

PART 3

Introduction

Ever wonder if *you might be a Dickhead*? Maybe you just can't put your finger on it, you are a little fuzzy about what it is to be a Dickhead. Or maybe you know a few Dickheads who do not know that they are, in fact, a Dickhead.

Maybe you've called someone (or many people) a Dickhead, or someone (or a lot of people) has called you a Dickhead. Maybe they are. Maybe you are.

We have heard it in the movies – actors calling people a Dickhead. In the movie *Twins* (1988), Julius (Arnold Schwarzenegger) gets what he wants from the genetic scientist when he says, "Tell us where our mother is … dickhead!" In *Patch Adams* (1998), Patch (Robin Williams) says to the Dean, "You have one responsibility to be a dickhead. How hard can that be? …" And in *Ted* (2012), John (Mark Wahlberg) casually asks his girlfriend, "How's your dickhead boss?"

In 1999, a well-known Australian businessman by the name of Dick Smith (yes, his real name) released a brand of matches called *Dickheads*. There's *The Dickhead Song* written by a fellow named Miles Betterman. There's also a *Dickhead* ringtone you can download onto your iPhone.

There's an Australian short Sci-Fi film nicely entitled, *I'm You, Dickhead*. And Mr. Floppy, an early 90s Australian punk rock band, released an album neatly titled *The Unbearable Lightness of Being a Dickhead*. But that's another story, as some of the lyrics in some of the songs seem to deal with an anatomical part of a man's body. We won't go there in this book.

Some people call other people simply *Dick*s or more colorfully, *Dickbrains*. But *Dickhead* seems to be the word of choice for many when wishing to let someone know that they are being an idiot or retard. The word dickhead has become an international word that is used and understood around the globe.

So what is a Dickhead and, importantly, what makes someone a Dickhead?

If you google the word *Dickhead*, you are likely to find words such as rude, selfish, unrealistic, stupid, disrespectful, unmannerly, obnoxious, irritating and annoying. You might find broader definitions, such as someone who just doesn't get it, doesn't want to listen to reason, or someone who just seems to be from another planet, someone we all wish would simply go home.

Dickheads are so often pathetic, arrogant, self-centered know-it-alls who believe that they are better or smarter than others – special. They are often thoughtless, either totally oblivious to or care less about the inconvenience or hardship that they may cause others. Dickheads are all around us, and the big ones are best avoided.

This book sets out 100 simple questions. Under each question, you are provided multiple choice answers. You simply need to circle the answers that apply to you. You can choose more than one answer under each question. If in doubt, choose all answers that *might* apply to you. By answering all of the 100 questions, you are able to create a *DH Score*. This score enables you to determine whether you are a Dickhead, kind of a Dickhead, or not a Dickhead, and if not, how close you may be to becoming a Dickhead.

Before we get to the questions – take note that Cambridge and Merriam-Webster dictionaries both define a *Dickhead* as a "person" (not *man*) who... This supports the premise that a woman can also be a Dickhead.

Please note: In this book, the word *partner* refers to one's boyfriend, girlfriend, legal, common-law or self-proclaimed wife or husband, whether heterosexual or LGBT.

PART 1
In Public

QUESTION 1

When in public, do you:

R   Pick your nose and look at what you picked.

U   Pick your nose and flick whatever you picked out into the air.

A   Pick your nose only when you know for sure that no one is looking or watching.

D   Pick your nose and eat what you have picked out.

H   Pick your nose and put what you picked out into your pocket to eat later.

QUESTION 2

You are out with friends. Someone asks everyone to put in their share of the bill. Do you:

R   Pull out your cell phone, open up the calculator app and figure out your exact share.

U   Lie to try to fool everyone into believing that your share is less than what it really is, knowing darn well that you ate and drank more than anyone else.

A   Put in a little extra, say 5% more than your share, and some for the tip.

D   Tell the others that you forgot your wallet and that you will pay them back at another time, and you don't.

H   Immediately go to the restroom and stay there for a while hoping that someone will pay for your share, and you somehow always forget to pay them back.

QUESTION 3

When at a restaurant and you want to get the server's attention, do you:

R   Wave your napkin in the air.

U   Snap your fingers in the air.

A   Try to make eye contact or raise your finger but don't wave that finger around in the air.

D   Clap your hands 2 or 3 times in the air.

H   Yell out something like, "Hey dickhead, how about some service over here."

QUESTION 4

When entering a public building, do you:

R   Never have the time to hold the door for someone else.

U   Not think about holding the door for someone. Why should you? People never hold the door for you.

A   Hold the door open for the person in front of or behind you when it's not awkward to do so, and when that person is close enough so that you don't have to stand there too long holding the door open.

D   Pay no attention to those in front of or behind you. Once you are through the door, you let go of the door regardless of someone being right in front of or right behind you.

H   Hold the door for a few seconds. If the person in front of or behind you doesn't get to the door in time to grab the opened door, you let go. That's their tough luck.

QUESTION 5

When in public, which of the following are OK with you?

R   Readjusting your boys (balls) or girls (breasts).

U   Touching, scratching or playing with your boys or girls.

A   None of the things on this page if you think others might see you doing it.

D   Scratching your butt hole.

H   Touching, scratching or playing with your partner's boys or girls.

QUESTION 6

Would you wear a T-shirt that has one of the following printed on it?

R   A cartoon image of a penis.

U   An image of a real penis.

A   An image of the front cover of this book.

D   An image of your penis or of your friend's penis.

H   An image of your breasts or of your friend's breasts.

QUESTION 7

How do you feel about farting in a crowded elevator?

R   It's OK to do it as long as it's silent.

U   Why not, everyone does it.

A   It's best to hold it and get off at the next floor and find a corner or a noisy place and then let it rip. But if you can't hold it, you cough loudly as you let it rip. This may muffle the noise of your fart and throw others off as to the direct source of the smell of your fart.

D   No problem. The more the merrier, the bigger and smellier the better.

H   Your personal philosophy is that when it wants out – let it out.

QUESTION 8

When using a public toilet, say at a department store or in a restaurant, do you:

R   Use a full roll of toilet paper to cover the seat before sitting down.

U   Take a selfie when finished, just before flushing.

A   Squat so that your bum, fanny, checks … doesn't need to touch the seat, or, if you've got the squirts (diarrhea), you use half a roll of toilet paper to cover the seat. You then do what you gotta do.

D   Miss getting your stuff into the toilet and leave those things on the floor near the toilet when you leave.

H   Fail to flush when finished, leaving your stuff for others to see and smell.

QUESTION 9

If you are working out at a gym, would you or do you:

R   Leave your sweat on the benches and machines.

U   Chat with the person working out on the bench or machine you are waiting to use.

A   Practice proper gym etiquette. You carry a sweat towel with you and wipe up after yourself. You know that chatting with those at the gym is for after finishing at the gym. You are also considerate of others at the gym and don't do things that annoy others.

D   Smell bad, grunt loudly as if you're pooping a large rock, leave weights on the bars or on the floor, and or walk around the gym as if you did poop a large rock – trying to show off your muscles or tight glutes.

H   Fart just before you move on to the next bench, machine or area in the gym.

QUESTION 10

If someone is smoking in a non-smoking area of a restaurant, would you:

R   Politely remind that person that it's a non-smoking area and then ask him or her if he or she would stop smoking.

U   Save up a fart and then stand next to the smoker's table and fart.

A   Ask the server at that restaurant for a different table and don't allow the smoker to ruin your day or evening. Or you get up and leave and go to a different restaurant.

D   Walk over to the smoker's table then stick your finger deep into your throat and barf all over the smoker's food and table.

H   Call the smoker a Dickhead.

(If you do smoke and do it in non-smoking areas, give yourself an extra 50 points on the score page for Part 1.)

QUESTION 11

When walking on a busy sidewalk, walkway, footpath or in a crowded area, do you:

R   Walk slowly in the middle.

U   Walk against the main flow of traffic. In other words, if most people walking in the direction that you are heading are walking on the right side, you walk on the left side.

A   Walk with the flow and at the same speed or pace as the flow. You also step to one side of the flow before you stop or to use your phone or tablet.

D   Stop suddenly and stand where you stopped when you; get a phone call, email or text; answer and talk on the phone; read the email or text; or reply to that email or text.

H   Talk on the phone, look at emails and texts, send emails and texts, and play games on your phone or tablets while walking.

QUESTION 12

You are waiting in a long line/ queue at the store. Do you:

R   Look for your discount coupons *after* everything has been rung up.

U   Forget to bring your wallet or cash and realize that you forgot when it's time to pay.

A   Prepare to pay when you're next in line by getting out your coupons, wallet or money. You pay with bills/notes and pocket any coins for another less crowded day. Better yet, you use a swipe credit or debit card.

D   Insist on paying the exact amount, digging into your purse, pockets or the bottom of your bag to find that last cent *after* everything has been rung up, while those behind you wait for you to pay.

H   Wait until the total shows up on the register and then start digging into your bag, purse or pockets to find your wallet or money so that you can pay.

QUESTION 13

When waiting for an elevator, do you:

R   Insist on being the first person to get on.

U   Rush in as soon as the door opens, not letting those who may want off to get off.

A   Stand to the side of the door and when the door opens, you let those who want to get off to get off before you get on. You also hold the door for those who may need help or a little extra time to get on the elevator, such as an old or disabled person.

D   Stand in front of the door and remain standing there when the door opens. You are oblivious of old people, pregnant women, women with babies and any disabled person who wish to get off or are also waiting to get on the same elevator.

H   Try to squeeze into the elevator when it's full rather than wait for the next one.

QUESTION 14

When you have a cold or the flu, and you are in a public place, would you or do you:

R   Let snot (mucus) drip out of your nose and use your sleeve to wipe it up.

U   Suck or snort in your snot rather than use a tissue to blow your nose.

A   Go straight home and stay home. You don't go out in public when sick unless it's truly necessary to do so, for instance, to buy food or medicine. You don't go to school or work or ride on public transportation. You don't want to pass on whatever virus or infectious illness you have onto others.

D   Put your finger over one nostril and shoot the snot out onto the ground when your nose fills up with snot.

H   Cough and sneeze and not care where your snot and germs may go.

QUESTION 15

When using a pedestrian crossing/crosswalk, do you:

R   Not bother to pick up your pace, not walk a little faster to get to the other side when the walk signal starts flashing red.

U   Take your time to get to the other side when the walk signal has turned red.

A   Look both ways before stepping into a pedestrian crossing, even if the walk signal is green. You know many Dickheads have a car driver's license. You also know that this means that even if the walk signal is green, it's no guarantee that a Dickhead driving a car will see you or stop for you.

D   Not care if the walk signal is green or red. You cross whenever you want. You like to play games with those in cars and you dare them to not stop for you or to hit you.

H   Expect drivers to see you and stop for you when in a pedestrian crossing.

QUESTION 16

If you fart in an elevator when with your friends or partner and others you don't know who are in the elevator with you hear it, what would you do?

R   Quickly get off at the next floor.

U   Say out loudly, "Who farted?"

A   Stand there and smile. You don't say anything. We are all human, we all fart.

D   Blame it on your friends or partner saying something out loud like, "Hey, don't fart in here."

H   Compliment yourself out loud with something like, "Great fart. That's sure to leave skid (poop) marks."

QUESTION 17

When in a store, when would you use the express checkout lane if you have more than the maximum number of items for that checkout?

R   When you have one or two items more than the express lane maximum amount.

U   Only when there isn't anyone waiting in that lane.

A   Never, unless the checkout person calls you over to use that lane when there is no one in the lane.

D   Whenever you want, even when you have a full shopping cart.

H   Whenever you are in a hurry, regardless of the number of items you have.

QUESTION 18

When at a department store or hotel, do you talk with others:

D   At the bottom, in the middle or at the top of the stairs.

D   Right in front of the elevator door.

D   At the top of the escalator right where you step off.

D   In the doorway or the middle of the entrance to the department store or hotel.

A   None of the above.

QUESTION 19

When walking on a sidewalk, walkway, footpath, or in a crowded area and someone is walking directly toward you, would you or do you:

R   Yell out something like, "Get out of my way dickhead."

U   Continue walking where you are. They can move. You were there first.

A   Make eye contact to determine if that person looks as if they will move to one side. If it doesn't, you move to one side so that they can pass by without bumping into you.

D   Let them bump into you so that you can show them how tough you are.

H   Play chicken with them. You want to see how close they dare get to you before one of you moves.

QUESTION 20

When walking on a sidewalk, walkway, footpath, or in a crowded area and someone is approaching from behind you, would you or do you:

R   Fail to recognize that there is someone behind you who wishes to get past you, to get ahead of you.

U   Keep walking. They can find a way to pass by you when they are ready to pass.

A   Stay alert so to recognize when there is someone approaching from behind you. You enable them to get past you easily when they are ready to pass.

D   Show them who's boss by forcing them to walk out into the street in order to pass you if they want to get past you.

H   Swerve to the right and left so that they can't get past you.

QUESTION 21

When you are waiting in a long line and the person in front of you farts, and you don't want to step out of the line, you:

R   Laugh, loudly. If the fart stinks, you breathe through your mouth. If that doesn't work, you stick breath mints in your nose to neutralize the smell of the fart.

U   Say something to the person, like, "Hey dickhead. Go fart somewhere else."

A   Let it go. You breathe normally. If the fart stinks, you use your sleeve when you breathe to help filter out the smell of the fart.

D   Say something out loud, like, "Smells like someone pooped in their pants" – even if the fart doesn't smell.

H   Fight fire with fire. You retaliate by turning around (your butt facing him or her) and fart an even louder, smellier fart.

QUESTION 22

When you are waiting in a long line, for instance at a sporting event, would you:

R   Sing Karaoke while you wait in line.

U   Play a jaw harp, mouth organ or guitar while you wait so that those near and far from you can hear you play.

A   Behave yourself. You consider those around you. You are quiet, allow others their space and you don't mess with their stuff.

D   Argue or become verbally or physically aggressive with those around you waiting in line. You just can't wait to start a fight.

H   Get drunk or stoned while waiting. You think the party started, so for you anything and everything goes. You litter and act like a 5 year old. You pee on buildings, mess with, even destroy, other people's stuff, and find it difficult to remember anything the next day.

QUESTION 23

When at the supermarket, do you:

R   Look for outdated or damaged food and then dicker (haggle) with the manager for a discount on those items.

U   Leave your shopping cart in the middle of the isle while you look for your favorite cereal or pop tarts.

A   Let the person behind you in the check-out line who only has a few things to go in front of you when you have a lot of things.

D   Run to get in front of an old person, a pregnant woman, or someone who is disabled who is about to stand in a checkout line so that you can get there before they do.

H   Stand in the middle of an isle to talk with someone, read or send an email or text or to talk on the phone – blocking the isle. You are too busy talking, reading or sending messages that you don't recognize or move for others in that isle.

QUESTION 24

When speaking on your phone when in public, do you:

R　　Keep your voice down and try not to bother the people around you.

U　　Speak in your normal full voice volume. (For some people, that's pretty loud.)

A　　Keep your voice down, keep the conversation short, and tell the person you are talking to that you will call them back as soon as you are somewhere that's more private.

D　　Keep talking on your phone when it is bothering people around you. Screw them. You believe that it's a free country and, there-fore, can do whatever you want to do.

H　　Speak at an increased volume. You believe that since the person you are talking to is far away, you have to speak loudly other-wise that person won't be able to hear you.

QUESTION 25

Do you thank people you don't know when they do something for you, for instance, when someone holds the door open for you at your favorite coffee shop?

R   Usually.

U   Only when you are having a good day.

A   Yes, always. Thanking someone is so easy for you to do. You know that doing so might just make someone else's day a little nicer.

D   Only when that person is cute, sexy, has a nice butt, has a tight body or package, or has big pecs or boobs.

H   No, why should you. You don't know that person and they don't know you.

QUESTION 26

When in public and you need to sneeze or cough, do you usually:

R   Cover your mouth with your hand and then wash your hands as soon as practical.

U   Use your sleeve to cover your mouth when you sneeze or cough.

A   Use a tissue or handkerchief to cover your nose and mouth when you sneeze or cough. Before touching anything in public, you wash your hands with the disinfectant gel or wipes that you always carry with you.

D   Let it flow into the air and onto others near you. You don't want to get snot on your hands or sleeves and can't be bothered to carry tissues or hand disinfectant with you.

H   Not think about it. You believe that sneezing or coughing into the air and onto people and things won't make others sick.

QUESTION 27

When on an escalator, do you:

R   Allow your kids or the people you are with to play on the escalator.

U   Stand in the middle of an escalator that is wide enough for two people, and not notice when others are behind you who may wish to pass and get in front of you.

A   Stand to one side and simply go up and down without any drama.

D   Stop and stand right where you step off the escalator to decide which direction you will go. You see no need to step to one side when you get off so that you won't block or prevent others from getting off when they need to step off.

H   Stand in the middle of an escalator that is wide enough for two people and don't move over to one side when you notice there are people behind you who may wish to pass and get in front of you.

QUESTION 28

When at a restaurant and the server asks you if you are ready to order, do you:

R   Tell the server that it's your birthday and that you want a free meal and dessert.

U   Ask the server what's good, and after they make their recommendations, you say something like, "That doesn't sound good."

A   Tell the server what you want. If you haven't decided, you ask the server to check back in a few minutes, and when the server comes back, you are ready to order.

D   Tell the server that you are ready when you haven't decided and then hem and haw while you try to decide what you want.

H   Say you're not ready, then continue to talk with your friends. When the server comes back, you say you need more time to decide and to check back later, again and again.

QUESTION 29

When walking on a sidewalk, walkway, footpath, or in a crowded area, do you:

R   Throw your trash on the ground.

U   Spit out your gum or whatever is in your mouth onto the ground.

A   Look for a garbage bin when you have trash, keep things in your mouth, and share the sidewalk, walkway, footpath, or crowded area with others. You move to one side before stopping and to allow others to get past you.

D   Stop where you were walking to talk to a friend you happen to meet – just like a dog stops when it feels like pooping – on the spot.

H   Walk side by side with your friends so to create a line of people across the sidewalk, walkway, footpath, or crowded area, thereby blocking and stopping others coming toward or from behind you who wish to pass you.

PART 1 SCORE PAGE

Write down below the number of Rs, Us, As, Ds, and Hs you circled in Questions 1 – 29. (Remember that you can circle more than one answer for each question.) Now do the math.

Example

R $\underline{8}$ x 2 = $\underline{16}$
U $\underline{6}$ x 3 = $\underline{18}$
A $\underline{7}$ x 3 = $\underline{21}$
D $\underline{5}$ x 5 = $\underline{25}$
H $\underline{6}$ x 4 = $\underline{24}$

Add R + U + D + H then subtract A
R (16) + U (18) + D (25) + H (24) – A (21) = $\underline{62}$

Your Turn

R   _____ x 2 = _____
U   _____ x 3 = _____
A   _____ x 3 = _____
D   _____ x 5 = _____
H   _____ x 4 = _____

R + U + D + H – A (+ the extra 50 Points from Question 10, if it applies to you.)

Total points for Part 1

PART 2
Getting Around

QUESTION 30

When riding on the bus, train or subway, do you:

R   Eat noisy food, like cheese puffs, rice crackers or potato or corn chips.

U   Slurp a big crushed ice drink or constantly blow into a cup of hot coffee or on a hot burrito.

A   Brush your hair, stick things in your ears or nose and pull things out, scratch your head to get rid of any lice or dandruff, or put on lip stick or hand cream.

D   Eat smelling food, such as a tuna fish sandwich, bowl of sauerkraut or a piece of semi-soft Limburger cheese.

H   Wait until you get off the bus, train or subway to do any of these things.

QUESTION 31

When driving your car, do you:

R   Change lanes without looking first.

U   Drive side by side with the car next to you.

A   Speed up when someone is trying to pass you.

D   Linger in other drivers' blind spot.

H   Stay alert and keep an eye on other drivers. You know that the other drivers just might be a Dickhead.

QUESTION 32

When driving, do you:

R   Turn on the turn indicator as you are making the turn but not before.

U   Turn on the turn indicator at about 6 feet (2 meters) before wanting to turn.

A   Turn on the turn indicator after you have made your turn.

D   Keep the turn indicator on at all times so that you don't forget to use it when you turn.

H   Turn on the turn indicator based on the speed that you are traveling and on the road conditions, but not less than approximately 15 – 30 feet (5 – 10 meters) before turning.

QUESTION 33

When on a plane, do you:

R   Pull on the back of the seat in front of you when you want to get up from your seat.

U   Fail to turn off your phone, tablet or computer when there is an announcement to do so, for instance, before take off or landing. You believe that such announcements only apply to the other passengers.

A   Leave the pee you sprayed all over the lavatory floor (due to unexpected turbulence when you were peeing) so that the other passengers can unknowingly mop up your pee with their socks when they walk into the lavatory.

D   Kick the seat in front of you.

H   Use the hand rests (not the seat in front of you) to help you to get up from your seat. You do your utmost to not kick, knock or pull on the seat in front of you or annoy, bother or inconvenience other passengers on the plane.

QUESTION 34

When riding on a plane, train, bus or subway, do you:

R   Stink (have BO) or reek of garlic.

U   Allow your body to lean onto someone you don't know who is seated next to you.

A   Fall asleep on the shoulder of someone you don't know who is sitting next to you.

D   Sit with your mouth wide open, snore or drool, or all of the above.

H   Smell kind of nice, allow the person sitting next to you to have and use their space by keeping your body parts in your part of your seat, and always ensure that your mouth doesn't hang open and that you don't snore or drool.

QUESTION 35

When driving your car, would you or do you:

R   Masturbate while you drive.

U   Drive without a license or drive on a suspended or canceled license.

A   Drive when you have been drinking or using drugs, had your brain removed or are about to fall asleep.

D   Watch TV or play games on your GPS device or TV while driving.

H   Follow the road rules most of the time. You never drive when you are sexually pre-occupied, or if you are physically, mentally, intellectually or legally unqualified to drive.

QUESTION 36

When riding on the bus, train or subway, do you:

R   Play music and games on your device without earphones or headphones, or even if you use them, the volume is so loud that the noise from your device can be heard by others.

U   Carry on a conversation with someone sitting across from you or sitting a few rows behind or in front of you, and speak loudly to compensate for the bus, train or subway internal or external noises.

A   Lie down on the seat next to you, or put your feet up on the seat in front of you.

D   Think it's perfectly OK to sneeze or cough into your hand and then touch everything around you, including the handrails, hanging straps, grab rails and tray tables.

H   Do none of the above. You're a thoughtful passenger. You have manners and you wish that others did too.

QUESTION 37

When driving your car, do you:

R   Read texts and emails.

U   Talk on your phone using the handset or hands free.

A   Close your eyes and take a nap.

D   Read and send text messages and emails and talk on your phone while you drive. You believe that you are great at multitasking and *know* that it's easy and safe for you to do so while driving.

H   Know that driving requires your full attention and that driving is not a time to test your multitasking skills.

QUESTION 38

Do you park in handicap parking spaces or zones when neither you nor your passengers are genuinely disabled?

(Being a Dickhead is a handicap but doesn't qualify for handicap parking.)

A   Yes, when you are in a hurry.

A   Sometimes, if there is more than one empty handicap parking space.

A   Only when you will be in the store for less than 5 or 10 minutes.

A   When it's raining or snowing or very cold outside.

H   No. Doing so would feel wrong to you.

QUESTION 39

You are in a crowded parking lot. You see someone pulling out. You grab that spot and get out of your car. You then notice that someone was waiting for that spot. Do you:

R   Not worry about it. You believe that everyone does it so why shouldn't you.

U   Pretend to answer your phone so that it appears that you don't see that person.

A   Extend your middle finger and wave it in the air. You want the driver to know, what they already know, that you're a Dickhead.

D   Yell out to the other person that you saw that spot first (even if you didn't).

H   Apologize. In a perfect world, you would get back in your car and find another parking spot. But sadly, we live in a world where size matters. So you look at the size of the other driver and make a judgment call.

QUESTION 40

When sitting on a crowded bus, train or subway, do you:

R   Feel it's OK for pregnant women and old or disabled people to stand up when you are sitting down – when you are fit enough to stand up.

U   Pretend to be asleep so you won't have to get up and give your seat to a pregnant woman or an old or disabled person.

A   Not care if a pregnant woman, old person or someone who is disabled has to stand. You got there first. First come first served is your motto.

D   Pay no attention. You believe life is easier for you if you are totally oblivious of those around you.

H   Offer your seat to anyone who appears to need it more than you. You always feel good about doing so.

QUESTION 41

When driving and you see someone using or about to use a pedestrian crossing, do you:

R   Not care. Streets are for cars not people.

U   Honk at those who are crossing the street and yell something nasty or rude at those waiting to cross.

A   Intentionally just miss hitting those who are in the pedestrian crossing.

D   Try to scare those crossing the street by flashing your lights and picking up speed so that it appears as if you are intending to run over those who are crossing.

H   Stop for those currently crossing the street and keep an eye on those who appear to want to cross the street. If there is no walk signal for people who wish to cross, you also stop (when safe) to let those wanting to cross, to cross (which is the law in some countries).

QUESTION 42

When driving, do you tailgate?

R   Only when you are in a hurry. For instance, when you're late for work or when you desperately need to take a poop.

U   Tailgate smailgate. You see nothing wrong with doing it.

A   Only when the driver in front of you is driving slower than you want to drive, even if the driver in front of you is driving at 25 mph (40 kph) over the speed limit.

D   Yes, when someone cuts you off. You feel that the driver needs to be taught a lesson and you are going to teach it.

H   You try not to tailgate. But if you find yourself driving too close to the car in front of you, you cautiously slow down (checking in your rear view mirror first to ensure that there isn't a Dickhead behind you who is tailgating you) so you can create more space between you and the car in front of you.

QUESTION 43

When on a bus, train or subway, would or do you:

R   Pretend to be pregnant, old, injured or disabled so that you can get a seat.

U   Spread out your things on the seat next to you so that no one will sit next to you.

A   Act sick or strange or look weird to discourage other passengers from sitting next to you. You like to have a lot of space when getting around, and don't want to share that space with others.

D   Stand next to the seat where you want to sit down and fart or act sick, strange or look weird. You feel that if done long enough, the person sitting there will get up and leave.

H   Understand that public transportation is just that, for public use. You realize that a bus, train or subway isn't your lounge room or your office. You behave yourself and you keep your things within your space.

QUESTION 44

When in a crowded parking lot, do you:

R   Take the parking space you see some-one else is waiting to park in.

U   Take up two car spaces to park your car.

A   Park in the handicap zone when your only handicap is that you're a real Dickhead.

D   Exit the parking lot by waiting in the middle of the exit that is wide enough for two cars (one to enter one to exit) rather than wait in the designated exit lane or to one side, the exit side. You prevent drivers who want to enter the parking lot from entering until after you exit because they can't get in to park, as you are waiting in the middle to exit.

H   Stay calm and go back home and use the Internet to shop or shop when the stores and parking lots aren't busy. You don't waste your time in crowded parking lots.

QUESTION 45

Would or do you double park?

R   What's double parking?

U   When you need to rush into a store to buy a loaf of bread or to use the store's toilet.

A   Whenever there isn't a place to park. Where else are you expected to park. It pisses you off when people complain when you do.

D   When you pick someone up who you are taking out on a date. You want to park in front of your date's apartment or house so that your date can see your car when you honk your horn to let your date know that you are waiting in your car.

H   Only in a genuine emergency or if you are picking up or letting off a very pregnant woman, an old person or someone who is disabled or injured. If you do, you try not to be double parked for more than a minute or two.

QUESTION 46

When riding on a bus, train or subway, do you:

R   Talk to yourself.

U   Mumble to yourself.

A   Make clicking sounds with your tongue or mouth.

D   Make sucking noises.

H   Sit quietly reading this book.☺

QUESTION 47

If you ride a bicycle in traffic or on the street, do you:

R   Talk on your phone or read or send texts or emails while riding.

U   Stop in the blind spot of cars in traffic, ride on the sidewalk, walkway or footpath, ride in a pedestrian crossing to cross the street, or ride in the middle of very narrow streets.

A   Ride between lanes of slow moving or stopped traffic and run through red lights.

D   Fail to wear a helmet and something bright so that you can be easily and quickly seen by those driving cars.

H   Know that there are many Dickheads driving cars on the street. You would like to ride a bicycle to get to and from work or to simply get around but you know that it may be too dangerous to do so.

QUESTION 48

When driving in an unfamiliar area, do you:

R   Enter the address or coordinates on your GPS device of the place you wish to go, while driving.

U   Think about sex.

A   Slow down and occasionally stop in the street to look around for street signs or to think if you should or shouldn't turn at the next street – when there are cars behind you.

D   Look at an old fashioned road atlas or fold-out road map while driving.

H   Find somewhere to get directions or pull over where safe and look at a map or enter the address or coordinates on your GPS device. Then proceed to go where you want to go.

QUESTION 49

When on a plane, bus, train or subway, do you:

R   Talk loudly to the person next to you.

U   Talk to someone you don't know who is reading a book, catching a few winks, or using their computer.

A   Talk loudly on your phone.

D   Clip, file or paint your fingernails or toenails.

H   Try to be a good passenger by keeping your voice down and trying not to bother others on the plane, bus, train or subway. You give others the personal space and peace and quiet you yourself would want. You wait to get home to clip, file or paint your fingernails and toenails.

QUESTION 50

When flying in economy class, do you:

R   Stretch your feet out into the isle.

U   Turn around and tell the person sitting behind you that you are going to recline your seat, and you do so, not so slowly.

A   Demonstrate your drumming skills to the passenger sitting in front of you by drumming on the seat in front of you – their seat.

D   Drop your seat back to full recline without warning the person sitting behind you that you are about to do so.

H   Aim to be a considerate passenger. You don't stick your feet out in the isle nor do you unnecessarily touch or mess with the seat in front of you. You refrain from reclining your seat and send a polite but firm complaint to the airline company about the lack of space to recline. You know that if enough people do complain, the airlines may make a change.

QUESTION 51

When in your friend's car and you have trash, such as food wrappers, chewed gum or an empty or partly filled drink can, would you or do you:

R   Toss it in the back seat of their car.

U   Throw it on the floor of your friend's car.

A   Throw it out the window.

D   Stick the trash between the seats when your friend is busy maneuvering a tight bend or curve in the road or passing another car at high speed so that he or she doesn't see you doing it.

H   Ask your friend if he or she has a trash bin or an empty plastic bag in their car. If he or she doesn't, you keep the trash and throw it away when you get out of the car and have found a proper trash bin or garbage can.

QUESTION 52

If you ride a motorcycle in traffic or on the street, do you:

R   Weave through moving or stationary traffic, dart in and out of lanes, or linger and stop in the blind spots of cars near you.

U   Ride wearing sandals, thongs, no shoes, short pants or no pants, or totally naked.

A   Ride when you are drunk, unlicensed or on a motorcycle that's too big or too powerful for you.

D   Drive at high speeds or try to be Evel Knievel by doing things like pulling wheelies or standing on the seat while riding.

H   Take care not to be a Dickhead when riding your motorcycle in traffic or on the street. You know that you need to know what you are doing when riding, to be careful and always ride defensively – ride knowing that some Dickhead driving in traffic or on the street could really mess up your life.

QUESTION 53

What do you think about road rules? Do you:

R   Follow the rules you like and ignore the rules that you don't like.

U   Follow the rules exactly as they are set out, even if, for instance, that means waiting for a traffic light in the middle of nowhere to turn green, or driving slower than the traffic around you or faster than is safe under the current circumstances, like rain or snow, so that you can obey the posted speed limit.

A   Not know what the road rules are.

D   Think that they don't apply to you since you *know* that you are a great driver and can decide for yourself how to drive.

H   Follow the rules. You might break a few rules when it's objectively safe to do so, such as when no other cars are in sight and doing so could not possibly have a negative effect on or injury others or be a risk to your safety.

QUESTION 54

When getting on the bus, train or subway, do you:

R   Fart. You like to let others know that you and your various body noises and smells will be riding with them.

U   Try to get on while passengers are still getting off thus stopping the flow of people wishing to get off.

A   Knock over old or disabled people so that you can get on and get a seat before they do.

D   Stand in the doorway talking on your phone or talking with someone who is seeing you off or who is waiting for you to get on.

H   Wait patiently for those who want off to get off, then you get on. You don't knock over old or disabled people. In fact, you are such a mannered individual that you take the time to help old or disabled people to get on.

PART 2 SCORE PAGE

Write down below the number of Rs, Us, As, Ds, and Hs you circled in Questions 30 – 54, and do the math.

R   _____ x 3 = _____
U   _____ x 2 = _____
A   _____ x 5 = _____
D   _____ x 4 = _____
H   _____ x 3 = _____

Add R + U + A + D – H

Total points for Part 2 [   ]

PART 3
Relationships

QUESTION 55

When you ask someone out on a date or you are asked out on a date, do you:

R   Expect that you will get laid.

U   Ask your date to be laid.

A   Pay for the date only if it means that you are likely to get laid.

D   Plan to go dutch or to pay and don't expect or ask to be laid.

H   Anticipate getting laid if you pay. Your philosophy is that if you pay, you should get laid.

QUESTION 56

Do you say thank you to your partner?

R   No. Why should you. Partners are
expected to do things for their partner. You
believe that being a partner means never
having to say sorry or thank you.

U   Never, is your philosophy. You believe
that if you start thanking your partner, he or
she will expect you to thank them all the
time. For you, that would be a drag.

A   Only if it will get you laid.

D   Yes, you do. Sometimes you do even
more. Sometimes you follow through with
action in addition to your words. You might,
for instance, give your partner a hug or small
gift or surprise.

H   Only when your partner asks you to or
demands that you thank them.

QUESTION 57

When on a date, do you:

R   Talk only about yourself and change the subject back to yourself each time your date tries to talk about anything other than about you. For you, this is not bragging. It's letting your date know how great you are and the great things you have done.

U   Spend most of the time reading text messages and emails, replying to those texts and emails, or playing games on your phone or tablet.

A   Talk about your ex-partner or other people you have dated and go into detail what made them Dickheads. You fail to tell your date that *you* were the real Dickhead.

D   Turn off your phone and tablet and devote the time to learn more about and to enjoy your time with the person you are with.

H   Wish that you were with someone else.

QUESTION 58

If you are in a friend's swimming pool and you have to go number 1 or 2, what do you do?

R   You can't be bothered to get out of the pool to use the toilet so you do it in your swimsuit.

U   You pull down your swimsuit and do it in the pool. You get out quickly, before others spot the yellow stuff or that brown thing you left floating in the pool.

A   You pee or poop or do both and then accuse the person who is near you in the pool for doing number 1 and or 2 in the pool.

D   None of the above. You don't swim in your friend's pool (or any public pool) since some who do – do do the above.

H   Sometimes you go number 1 in your friend's pool but not too often. But you never do number 2.

QUESTION 59

Immediately after having sex, do you:

R   Roll over and play dead and pretend that it never happened.

U   Roll over and play dead and wish that it never happened.

A   Think nothing of it and get up and turn on the TV or make yourself a cup of tea, or both.

D   Stay awake, smile and politely ask for more and happily give more.

H   Sigh, roll over and go to sleep.

QUESTION 60

Someone asks you to a dinner party and tells you that you can bring someone. Would you bring:

R   Someone you know those who will be at the party don't like. You believe that others should respect your wishes to bring whoever you decide to bring with you.

U   Someone who had a one-nighter or an affair with the partner of the host of the party.

A   The ex-partner of someone who will be at the party.

D   The host's grandma. You know that everyone likes good old grandma.

H   No one. Your aim is to pick someone up at the party, including grandma.

QUESTION 61

When riding in your friend's car, would you:

R   Throw up in their car. You can't be bothered to ask them to pull over so that you can barf outside the car.

U   Be totally OK with riding in their car if your shoes had fresh dog poop stuck to the bottom.

A   See no problem with riding in their car if your shoes had what looked like dog poop stuck to the bottom of your shoes, but was in fact only mud.

D   Refrain from giving your friend advice or suggestions on how they could improve their driving skills. If their driving bugs you or you fear for your life when riding with them, you would be a Dickhead to get into their car the next time they want to drive.

H   Fart without warning.

QUESTION 62

When eating out at a nice restaurant, do you:

R   Use a toothpick, dental floss or your finger when at the table to get that spinach or steak out from between your teeth.

U   Burp and make other body noises or sounds at the table.

A   Walk around the restaurant looking for any rich or famous people among the other diners. If you spot any, you try to strike up a conversation with them, and take selfies.

D   Enjoy the atmosphere and food. Give the person you are with your full attention and follow proper dining etiquette. You leave the selfies for another time and place.

H   Cut your steak into small pieces before eating it (like your mother used to do for you when you were 10).

QUESTION 63

Do you really listen to your partner?

R   Only when your partner is saying nice things about you.

U   Never. You believe that your partner never has anything to say that's worth listening to.

A   Rarely, as you feel that your partner has no idea of what they are talking about. You feel that listening to what your partner says would be like listening to a dill pickle.

D   Yes. You are truly interested in knowing what's happening in your partner's life. You also want to know your partner's dreams, goals and aspirations. You know that listening to your partner enables you to help them to be happy and to reach their dreams, goals and aspirations, which makes you happy.

H   Sometimes, but most of the time, you don't care what your partner is saying.

QUESTION 64

You are in your car or your date's car on a first date, and you fart. What do you do?

R   Roll down the window quickly to let fresh air in and the bad smell out, even if it's raining or snowing or freezing outside.

U   Accuse your date of farting.

A   Say nothing, hoping that your date didn't hear it or doesn't smell it. You worry that your fart may have blown it for you. You start thinking about who you could go out with next weekend, believing that this one will never go out with you again if they did in fact hear or smell the fart.

D   Excuse yourself and maybe giggle or make a joke about it.

H   Blame the smell on the cows or nearby factory that aren't or isn't there, hoping your date isn't familiar with the local geography.

QUESTION 65

Do you keep your partner or friends waiting, for instance, if you had organized to meet them at a restaurant at 6?

R   Often, but you always have a good reason (excuse) for being late.

U   All the time. That's you. You believe that your partner and friends know that and expect and accept that from you.

A   You don't worry about things like that. You feel that if they don't like it when you are late, that's their problem.

D   Rarely. If it looks as if you will be late, you call them to let them know that you will be late. You tell them when you will be there, and you are there at the time you say you will be there.

H   Sometimes, like when the TV show you're watching hasn't finished yet.

QUESTION 66

When do you call your partner or friends to let them know that you will be late?

R   One hour after you were supposed to meet them.

U   You don't call them. You *know* that they will understand that you were too busy to call to let them know that you will be late and when you will be there.

A   30 minutes after you were supposed to be where you were to meet them.

D   At least 10 to 15 minutes before you are supposed to meet them. You apologize and let them know when you will be there. You ask them to wait for you or tell them to start without you.

H   A day before you are supposed to meet them because you know that you will be late, as you are always late.

QUESTION 67

You have a touch of diarrhea or haven't pooped for a week. You're at a friend's place and you need to use their toilet. You do, and the toilet backs up and overflows. Would you:

R   Wedge something in the toilet water tank so that the water stops filling the toilet bowl. You put the seat lid cover down, go out to your friend and you don't say anything to your friend.

U   Leave things as they are. You lay towels on the floor to soak up your stuff. You then go out to your friend and tell your friend that you need to go home, and you do.

A   Climb out the window and go home.

D   Talk a selfie, post it on Facebook, then tell your friend and help to clean it up.

H   Make a video and upload it on YouTube.

QUESTION 68

When out for a meal and some drinks with friends, do you:

R   Drink too much, so much that you almost barf, almost fall on the floor, almost pass out, and have a hard time remembering your name.

U   Drink so much that you barf up everything you ate and drank, then you pass out. You leave your friends with the chore of getting you home. You ruin their evening out. You just can't understand why they seem to *forget* to ask you to join them anymore.

A   Fart all night. You tell your friends that it's the bean burrito you ate for breakfast.

D   Act reasonably and responsibly. You enjoy the time with your friends.

H   Bore your friends talking about how great your life is when in fact your life is a real mess, nothing in your life is the way you want it to be.

QUESTION 69

When you see the number 69, what do you do?

R   Feel like eating a cherry Popsicle or going out to a sushi bar for a few clam sushi.

U   Think of the number 4761.

A   Sit down and remember all of the people you shared that number with.

D   Feel a bit horny.

H   Giggle, get embarrassed and blush.

QUESTION 70

You meet your partner for lunch during your lunch break from work. Do you:

R   Spend the time reading and sending text messages and emails or playing games on your phone or tablet.

U   Take out your computer and spend the time doing work stuff on your computer.

A   Talk about work or complain about your job or boss. Your partner listens to you but you fail to notice that your partner is so bored with what you're saying that he or she is wishing that they hadn't wasted their afternoon meeting you for lunch.

D   Talk with and listen to your partner. You don't talk about or do any work during lunch. You spend that time to bond even closer with your partner.

H   Eat, gaze into space and say nothing.

QUESTION 71

If a friend or partner asks for your advice or help, would you:

R   Ignore them. You're not interested. You think that it would be a waste of your time helping them to sort out their life.

U   Tell them that you are too busy, when in fact you aren't busy. You just don't want to be bothered with their grips, issues, problems or their trivial life.

A   Tell them that you have all the right answers to their problems. You then proceed to tell them what they need to do.

D   Listen to what they have to say and offer suggestions or advice. If you don't have the time when they ask, you organize with them a time and place when and where you can listen and help them, if you can.

H   Tell them you are interested in helping them, but you never make the time to do so.

QUESTION 72

When having sex with your partner or anyone for that matter, do you:

R   Do the wheelbarrow – that is, do it as he or she is facing forward so that you don't need to look him or her in the eyes while having sex.

U   Do what you like to do. For you, enjoying yourself is what sex is all about. After you have done your thing, you fart and then fall asleep.

A   Talk about your kids' rotting teeth, the overdue mortgage payment or the dog down the street with a serious diarrhea problem.

D   Communicate so that both of you know what the other likes. You both have fun and both of you get what you want from it.

H   Not say a word. You believe your duty is to lie there and let it in, or to put it in there.

QUESTION 73

The first time in bed with someone, would you:

R   Pull out all of your sex toys, including that two foot long hot-dog looking thing that you borrowed from a friend.

U   Not care if your sex toys or methods in bed frightens the other person. You don't care if the other person likes what's going on or is having fun.

A   Not ask the other person what he or she likes and enjoys in bed. You don't need to ask. You *know* what the other person likes and enjoys. You do it to them the way you *know* they want it. You are a real sex machine.

D   Find out what he or she likes so that both of you can enjoy each other and have fun together.

H   Not know the other person's name or care who they are. For you, it's how you do it, not who you do it to that counts.

QUESTION 74

You're in a car on a first date. You've been holding in a fart since getting into the car. You find that you can't hold the fart much longer. What do you do?

R   Make up a story about having a poop hole problem, going into detail so your date has a mental image of the problem. Then fart.

U   Sit on your hand and squeeze your butt cheeks together, releasing the fart gradually.

A   Tell your date that you forgot to return an important business call and need to stop and get out of the car to make that call.

D   Tell your date that you need to stop and get out for a second. You get out and let it rip.

H   Slide in and play the Led Zeppelin CD you keep with you for such occasions, really loud. This has in the past taken your dates' minds off what you are about to do – fart.

QUESTION 75

Would you or do you:

R   Make out with your partner on the sofa when your guests are sitting next to you on the sofa.

U   Have sex with your partner when your guests are sitting on the sofa where you are having sex.

A   Allow your dog to fart or to lick his or her parts or your guests' parts when your guests are sitting on your sofa.

D   Ensure that your guests are comfortable when on your sofa. You offer them food and beverage and ensure that nothing, including your or your dog's extracurricular activities, will mess with your guests' physical, mental or emotional well-being.

H   Allow your dog to hump your guests' leg when your guests are trying to relax on your sofa.

QUESTION 76

If visiting a friend and he or she isn't feeling well or it looks as if he or she is dealing with a personal problem, would you:

R   Stay and talk about how great your life is going.

U   Help yourself to a beer or glass of wine, get a few snacks from the fridge, turn on the TV, ask for a pillow, curl up on the sofa and not allow your friend to ruin your evening.

A   Order a pizza and hang around for a few hours. Better yet, make your own pizza in your friend's kitchen and stay the night.

D   Offer to help but politely excuse yourself and go if your friend doesn't ask you to stay. Even if your friend says it's OK to stay, you know when it's time to go and you go.

H   Ask your friend to help you with a personal problem of your own.

QUESTION 77

Do you:

R   Not bother to listen to or to consider advice or suggestions that your friends or family might offer you. You just *know* that whatever they advise or suggest is and will always be stupid or wrong.

U   Believe that the only right way to do something is your way.

A   Get upset with or lash out at friends or family when they offer sincere suggestions or advice that may be different from how you see things or think things should be done.

D   Listen to and consider what friends and family think and believe. You respect their opinions, ideas and thoughts and you are careful with their feelings.

H   Fail to realize that you just might have misunderstood or misinterpreted comments or the intentions of friends or family. You're a pig-head and this ruins your relationships.

PART 3 SCORE PAGE

Write down below the number of Rs, Us, As,
Ds, and Hs you circled in Questions 55 – 77.
Time to do some math again.

R   _____ x 4 = _____
U   _____ x 5 = _____
A   _____ x 3 = _____
D   _____ x 3 = _____
H   _____ x 2 = _____

Add R + U + A + H – D

Total points for Part 3

PART 4
Your Brain

QUESTION 78

When you use a friend's toilet, do you:

R   Not flush, thus leaving your pee or poop in the toilet when you leave.

U   Pee, poop and flush.

A   Flush a sock or hand towel down the toilet so that the next time your friend uses his or her toilet, it will overflow. You like to play jokes on your friends.

D   Leave poop marks on the inside of the toilet bowl.

H   Intentionally pee on the toilet seat and laugh as you do.

QUESTION 79

Would you or do you:

R   Ask a friend or family member who will be traveling overseas to bring back something for you that's bulky or that may require that they need to claim it at customs or may need to go through a customs search.

U   Usually not ask others to do things for you. If you do, you try not to impose on or inconvenience others. You do appreciate when others do things for you and you tell them or better yet show them that you do.

A   Ask someone to do something for you because you don't want to do it yourself.

D   Not bother to acknowledge or reply to an email from someone who has taken the time to reply to your question or request.

H   Not bother to pick up your pace, even if just a little, if someone is holding a door open for you, to let them know that you do appreciate them holding the door for you.

QUESTION 80

When eating out at an all-you-can-eat buffet, do you:

R   Take food from the buffet to taste to see if you like it and put it back (half eaten) when you don't like how it tasted.

U   Fill up one plate at a time and go back for seconds or thirds after you have finish your first or second plate. You know that there will still be food at the buffet when you are ready to fill up your next plate.

A   Sneeze or cough on the food at the buffet.

D   Have fun by walking around the buffet against the flow, that is, you start filling up your plate where others finish the buffet.

H   Fill up four or five plates and put some food in your handbag or the plastic bag you brought with you from home. You like those large prawns and tasty looking crab legs.

QUESTION 81

Do you:

R   Spit, anywhere and anytime you want.

U   Chew with your mouth closed and keep the things that are in your mouth, in your mouth.

A   Chew with your mouth open and let things drop out of your mouth when you chew.

D   Talk with your mouth full of food.

H   Let things drop out of your mouth even when you aren't chewing.

QUESTION 82

When you go to a party, do you or would you:

R   Have sex on the host's sofa, table or bed when others are still at the party.

U   Thank the host and go home when the party looks like it might be starting to wind down or when it's getting late. You're a well-mannered guest who is often asked to parties.

A   Forget to introduce the person you brought with you to the party to others at the party who have not yet met the person.

D   Aim to be the last person to leave the party. You like to be the last one there so that you can take all the left over food home with you when you leave.

H   Fall asleep in the host's bed, with or without the host, while the party is still going on.

QUESTION 83

Have you ever thought about:

R   Buying an inflatable girl or guy – a new *best-friend*.

U   What you would say to your partner if you did order an inflatable girl or guy and your partner were to ask you about your new friend that UPS or DHL delivered to your home when you weren't at home.

A   Having sex with an inflatable girl or guy.

D   Ordering and sending someone you like or don't like an inflatable girl or guy, so that they too can have a new *best-friend*.

H   Selling inflatable girls and guys on the Internet or from your garage.

QUESTION 84

When someone you know does something for you, do you:

R   Say nothing. You expect people to do things for you. You feel that you don't need to say anything.

U   Thank them with words followed by action. You *show* them that you appreciate what they do for you.

A   Grunt (then not say anything else). You *know* that they will know that a grunt from you is your way of saying "thank you".

D   Try to remember to thank them but sometimes you forget.

H   Thank them when what they do is something really special. But you feel that it's not necessary to thank people for the little things they do for you.

QUESTION 85

When you are wrong or have made a mistake, do you:

R   Never apologize. You *know* that you are never wrong and never make mistakes.

U   Apologize and learn from when you are wrong or have made a mistake.

A   Feel that you don't need to apologize. You believe that when you are wrong or have made a mistake it's because of other people, they caused you to be wrong or to make the mistake.

D   Rarely apologize. You don't want other people to think that they are smarter, wiser or better than you.

H   Apologize for all and everything even if it wasn't you who was wrong or made the mistake. This enables you and others to forget it and move on. This makes you feel like a real loser but that's OK because you know you are.

QUESTION 86

Do you truly believe:

R   You know everything there is to know.

U   There is and always will be others who know more than you know, that there is always something new to know and that you will never know all there is to know.

A   You know everything that's worth knowing.

D   You know a lot more than what most people know. You are simply smarter than most people. You believe that you are pretty darn smart.

H   No one knows anything you don't already know that would be valuable to or useful for you.

QUESTION 87

You drop something and someone brings it to your attention. Would you:

R   Tell the person to mind their own business.

U   Smile, say thank you and pick it up.

A   Pick it up and say nothing.

D   Mumble something that may or may not include the words "thank you".

H   Tell that person that you knew that you dropped it and say nothing more.

QUESTION 88

Do you believe that you:

R   Have a huge dick (penis) or the hottest boobs (breasts) in town, or both.

U   Are unique and may have special skills, knowledge or attributes that others may not have. You know that this makes you different from others, not better or lesser than.

A   Are a true sex god or sex goddess. You *know* that you are fantastic in bed. You know all the moves and positions and have your own code name for each of them. You call those codes out as you perform them on the person in bed with you. You truly believe that everyone wants to get in bed with you.

D   Are the smartest person you know.

H   Are great looking, a 10 out of 10. You are so proud of your looks that you look at yourself in anything that reflects your image, such as a store window, water glass, or your or anyone's cell phone or tablet screen.

QUESTION 89

Someone has gone beyond what is expected or goes out of their way to enable you to experience something special, do you:

R   Fail to thank them. You just couldn't be bothered to do so.

U   Thank them in person when they are doing or have done what they do or did for you. You might also follow up by thanking them again the next time you contact them. You might even send them a real snail mail card or give them a small gift of thanks.

A   Not want to thank them. You think doing so would create an obligation to pay them back one day, to do something for them.

D   Fail to call them or send them an email to thank them. You simply forget.

H   Not recognize what they had done for you or that they have gone out of their way.

QUESTION 90

When things aren't the way you want things to be in your life, do you:

R   Blame other people and make excuses.

U   Take a look in the mirror (at yourself). You know that we are often the reason why things aren't the way we want things to be in our life. You then take positive action to do something to fix or change those things.

A   Plot revenge on those you blame for the way things are in your life.

D   Believe that you can't change those things. In fact, you are afraid of making changes. You believe that you don't have what it takes to change. With that attitude, you don't, can't and won't.

H   Simply accept things for what and how they are. You believe that these things are beyond your control, that it's your destiny.

QUESTION 91

When at the supermarket, do you:

R   Squeeze the hell out of the fruit to test if it's ripe then put it back if it was ripe (now that it's bruised and too soft, squashed).

U   Do the right thing. You are gentle with the food and you treat the food as not being yours unless and until you have paid for it.

A   Drink or eat food (that you haven't paid for) while you shop. You aim to drink or eat it before getting to the checkout. You put the empty package or container on a shelf and don't pay for it. You believe the supermarket can afford to feed you while you shop.

D   Pick and eat the grapes or eat all of the free samples when the person sampling those things is on his or her break.

H   Crash your shopping cart/trolley into everything and everyone. You are too busy checking out the men or ladies in the store.

QUESTION 92

Do you:

R   Leave things the way they weren't. For instance, leave your trash where there was no trash, open a door that was closed and leave that door open after you walk in or leave, or leave (paint) your name, logo or some stupid drawing on someone's once clean wall.

U   Think before you act and act reasonably so that what you do will not inconvenience, interfere with or harm others.

A   Have a loud or stupid ring tone on your phone. You don't bother to turn your phone to manner mode (vibe) when you are out in public or on public transportation.

D   Drive to a gasoline station 50 miles away to save 2 cents a gallon on gasoline.

H   Allow your children or the people you are with to misbehave, for instance, to talk loudly, scream, run around or act like an idiot when in public or on public transportation.

QUESTION 93

When you have sex, do you:

R   Get drunk, loaded or stoned. You are so wasted that you don't really experience it for what it is. You can't remember what it was like or even who you did it with. You just can't figure out why the person you were with thinks that you are a real loser in bed.

U   Enjoy it and do what you can to help the other person or persons you are with to have a good time too.

A   Lie there like a dead tuna fish while the other person does all the work. You then later complain about how bad the sex was.

D   Get it over with as quickly as you can so that you can go to sleep.

H   Lie there wishing you weren't having sex with that person. You think about something or someone else, anything other than the person who is humping you or is being humped.

QUESTION 94

When at a restaurant, would you do any of the following so that you can get free food:

R   Bring a live or dead cockroach from home and stick it in the food after you have eaten about 80% of the food.

U   You never thought about doing these things and you have no plans to start.

A   Bring a rusty nail from home and stick that in the food.

D   Bring a wad of hair from your hair brush at home and stick it in your food right before calling the manager over to complain and demand the meal for free.

H   Leave a set of fake keys and a $2 pair of sunglasses on the table and slip out the back or front door of the restaurant – after finishing all but 10% of your meal.

QUESTION 95

Does it feel right and OK for you to:

R   Be nasty to or violent toward others or not allow others to be who they are or wish to be.

U   Be polite and kind to other people, as often as you can. You accept people for who they are or wish to be, but have a low level of tolerance for Dickheads. You hope that one day Dickheads will disappear.

A   Have sex with your partner's friend.

D   Try on a new swimsuit at the clothing or department store without wearing your underwear.

H   Fart when trying on a new swimsuit at the clothing or department store when you aren't wearing your underwear.

QUESTION 96

Do you:

R   Plan in the next 6 months to buy for yourself or for your partner or a friend a penis enlargement machine.

U   Refrain from doing any of the things in this question.

A   Shake hands with someone when you haven't bothered to wash your hands after toilet visits, coughing, blowing your nose, or scratching your butt.

D   Spit when you talk or let your mouth hang open when you walk.

H   Try to push other people's buttons or pull their strings (manipulate people).

QUESTION 97

When you see a friend unexpectedly in a crowded place, would you or do you:

R   Stop right where you are, for instance, in the middle of a walkway at a busy airport, and chat.

U   Say *Hi*, and if you have the time suggest going somewhere to talk or to move to the side to talk so that you don't disrupt the flow of people traffic or inconvenience others.

A   Stop for a minute then start walking with that friend so that the two of you can bump into people while you walk and talk.

D   Ignore that person by pretending that you don't see them so that you don't have to stop and talk with them.

H   Tell them that you are too busy to talk, that you have things to do and places to go, then walk away so you don't have to talk.

QUESTION 98

Do you:

R   Show up uninvited or unexpectedly at friends' and family members' homes.

U   Call before going to people's homes. You respect other people's privacy. If when you call they seem to be busy or don't come right out with an invitation, you take the hint. You suggest another time to visit. You don't put yourself in other people's private affairs unless invited.

A   Complain most or all of the time. You just can't resist sharing your hardships or troubles with others. You're a negative person and you allow this to have a negative effect on everything in your life.

D   Jump into the private conversations of people you know and don't know.

H   Invite yourself to other people's parties or special events, like a graduation party or wedding.

QUESTION 99

If you have a big honking zit on your face, would you:

R   Leave it and let it grow to see how big it will get.

U   Pop it or let it grow, but either way you put a band-aid over it. You might tell people that you cut yourself shaving or that you cut your face with your fingernail. But you never go out in public or allow others to see you with an uncovered big honking zit on your face.

A   Take a selfie and post it on Facebook.

D   Cover it up with massive amounts of makeup. You are sure no one will notice it.

H   Pop it and let it breathe. You're proud of it but you tell people it's a mosquito bite.

QUESTION 100

If someone knows more, can do more or has done more than you, do you:

R   Put down or criticize whatever it is.

U   Feel happy for them and even admire them. If it's something you would like to know or do yourself or that might help you to get more in life, you ask that person if they would share with you what they know.

A   Tell others who ask you about that person's knowledge, skills, achievements or experiences that their knowledge, skills, achievements or experiences aren't that great.

D   Ignore everything they say. You believe that you know more, could do more, or have done more than they do or have done, when in fact you might not, could not or have not. You're jealous, but won't admit that you are.

H   Let it bother you. You hate that person.

PART 4 SCORE PAGE

Write down below the number of Rs, Us, As, Ds, and Hs you circled in Questions 78 – 100. Time to do the math, one more time.

R   _____ x 5 = _____
U   _____ x 3 = _____
A   _____ x 4 = _____
D   _____ x 2 = _____
H   _____ x 3 = _____

Add R + A + D + H – U

Total points for Part 4

GRAND TOTAL

Add the points for Parts 1 (p. 36), 2 (p. 64), 3 (p. 90) and 4 and enter that number below.

What does your score mean?
Turn the next page and find out.

Are You A Dickhead? Let's find out.

Check Your Score

0 – 100 You're AOK. You aren't a Dickhead. Smile and give yourself a pat on the back. The world definitely needs more people like you.

101 – 200 You are usually OK but you may be a closet Dickhead. Do your friends and family a favor, stay in there and don't come out until you do some work on yourself so that you can score below 101.

201 – 300 You are a borderline Dickhead. You need to work on your manners and personality so that you don't become a big Dickhead. Your friends, family and even millions of people you don't know are depending on you to get into it and make some changes in who you are. The fewer Dickheads there are in world, the better the world will be.

More than 301 Congratulations *Dickhead*. You are a full blown true blue Dickhead. But hold on Dick. This isn't the time to be proud or the time to celebrate. It's time for you to start improving yourself. It's time that you become a better person. It's time to decide to make some serious changes in yourself. It's also time to say goodbye Dickhead and good luck.

Epilogue

There you have it, your official Dickhead Score. How did you do? How do you feel? *Are you a Dickhead?* Surprised? Don't worry. All of us do Dickhead things from time to time. But we need to aim to limit those times.

Maybe you are like me, thinking that for some reason Dickheads are drawn to you. It seems that the person who sits next to you on the bus or train, or is seated next to you or behind you when on a plane is always a Dickhead. It seems that the person who walks next to, in front of or behind you is always a Dickhead. Your boss is a Dickhead and heaven forbid, your neighbor is a big Dickhead. Dickheads just seemed to be everywhere. Maybe you ask yourself – Why?

The answer is quite simple. There are a lot of Dickheads in the world.

The world would be a better place if there were fewer Dickheads. We owe it to humanity to help our fellow human beings to determine if they are a Dickhead or kind of a Dickhead so they can stop being a Dickhead. We can do this if we:

- Buy this book for a friend who we think is a Dickhead. Maybe give it to that friend for his or her birthday.

- Leave this book in a friend's car or in his or her home.

- Leave it on our boss's or co-worker's desk.

- Leave it on our partner's or lover's pillow (the morning after unsatisfying sex).

- Buy this book and leave it on a table in or on a book shelf at our favorite coffee shop.

- Slip this book into a friend's bag or the bag of any Dickhead who works out, plays tennis, golf or squash or spends time where we do.

- Tell our friends about this book by posting a comment on Facebook, and help people we don't know to discover this book by posting a comment or review in a blog or on Amazon.

Thanks for reading. I sure hope that this book enables you or someone you know to stop being a Dickhead or from becoming a Dickhead. Not being a Dickhead is sure to mean more friends in your life and enjoying your life a lot more. Not being a Dickhead is certain to help make the planet a nicer place to live for us all.

May all of you live a long, happy and
dickhead free life.

If you enjoyed this book, your review
on Amazon or your favorite online book
seller's website, Facebook or other social
media site or blog would certainly be
most appreciated.

Another book by Fred Mogura

What Friends SHOULD Do

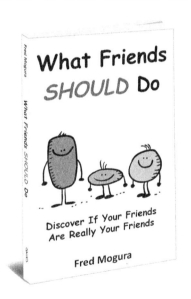

Now available on Amazon and on your
favorite book sellers' websites.
ISBN 978-0-9872677-8-8